My Home is High

Written by David Bennet Illustrated by Andrew Plant

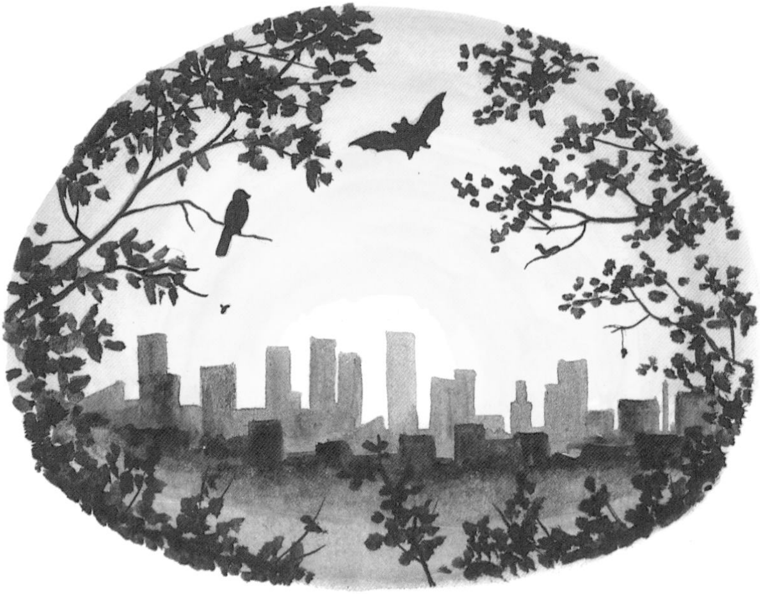

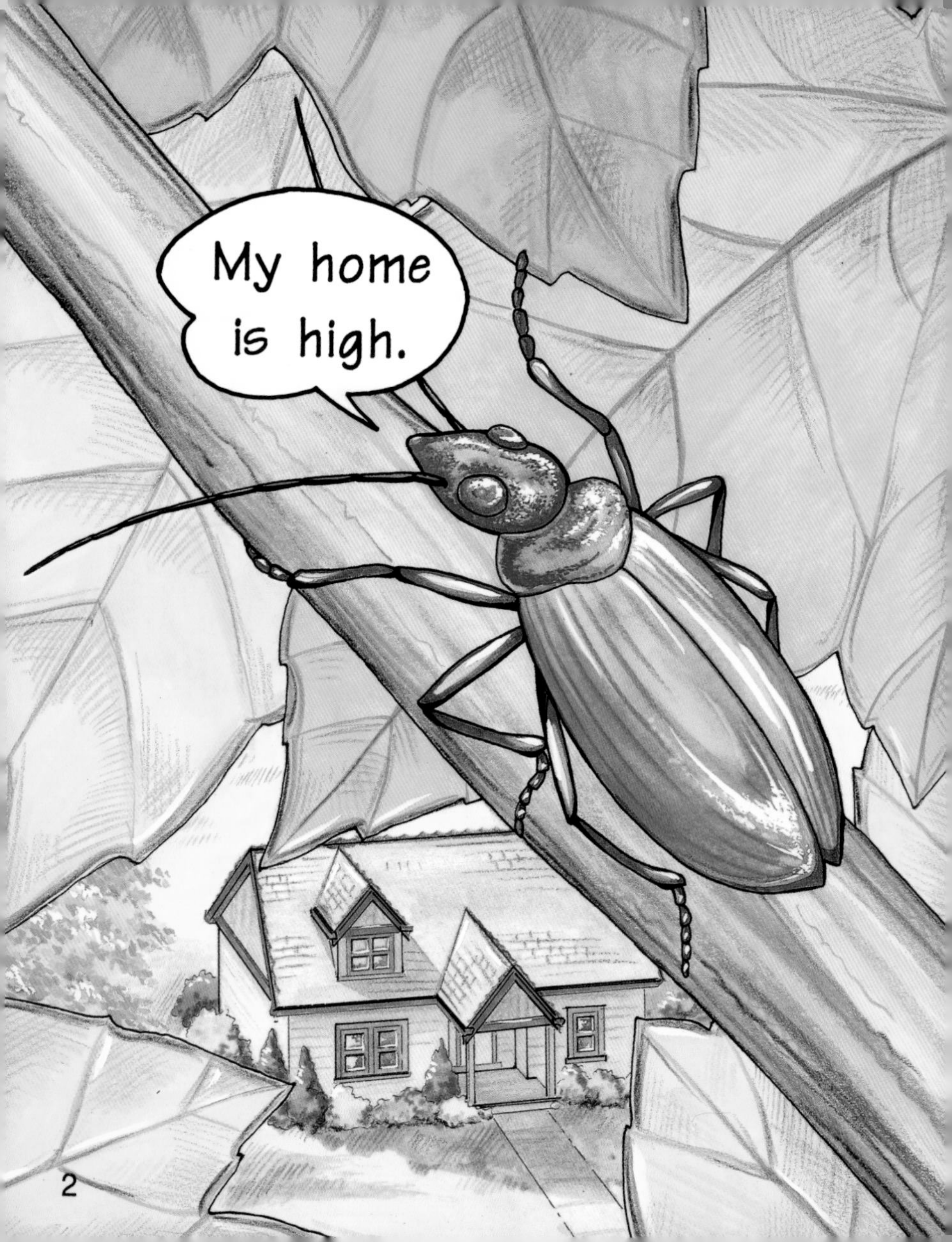
My home is high.

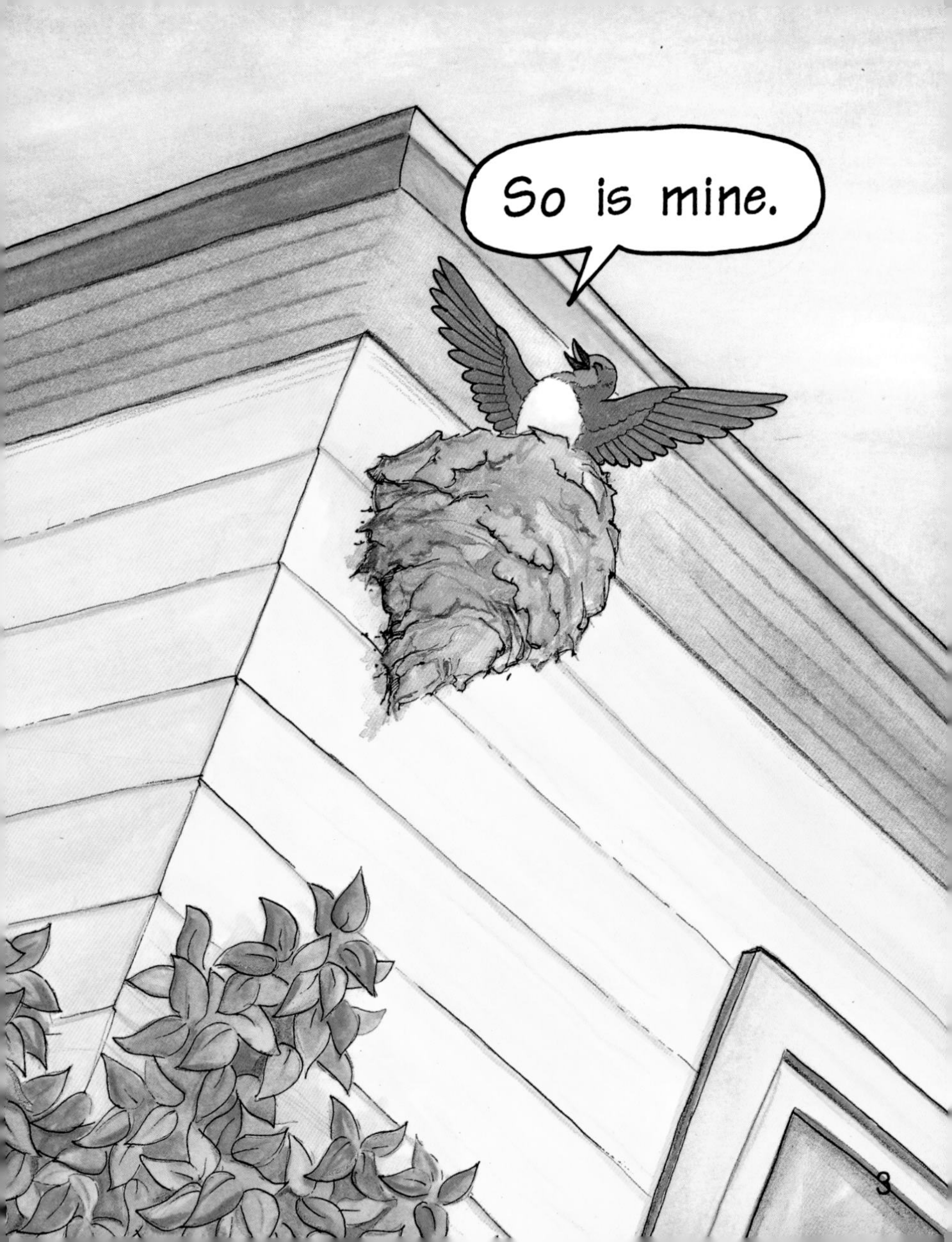
So is mine.

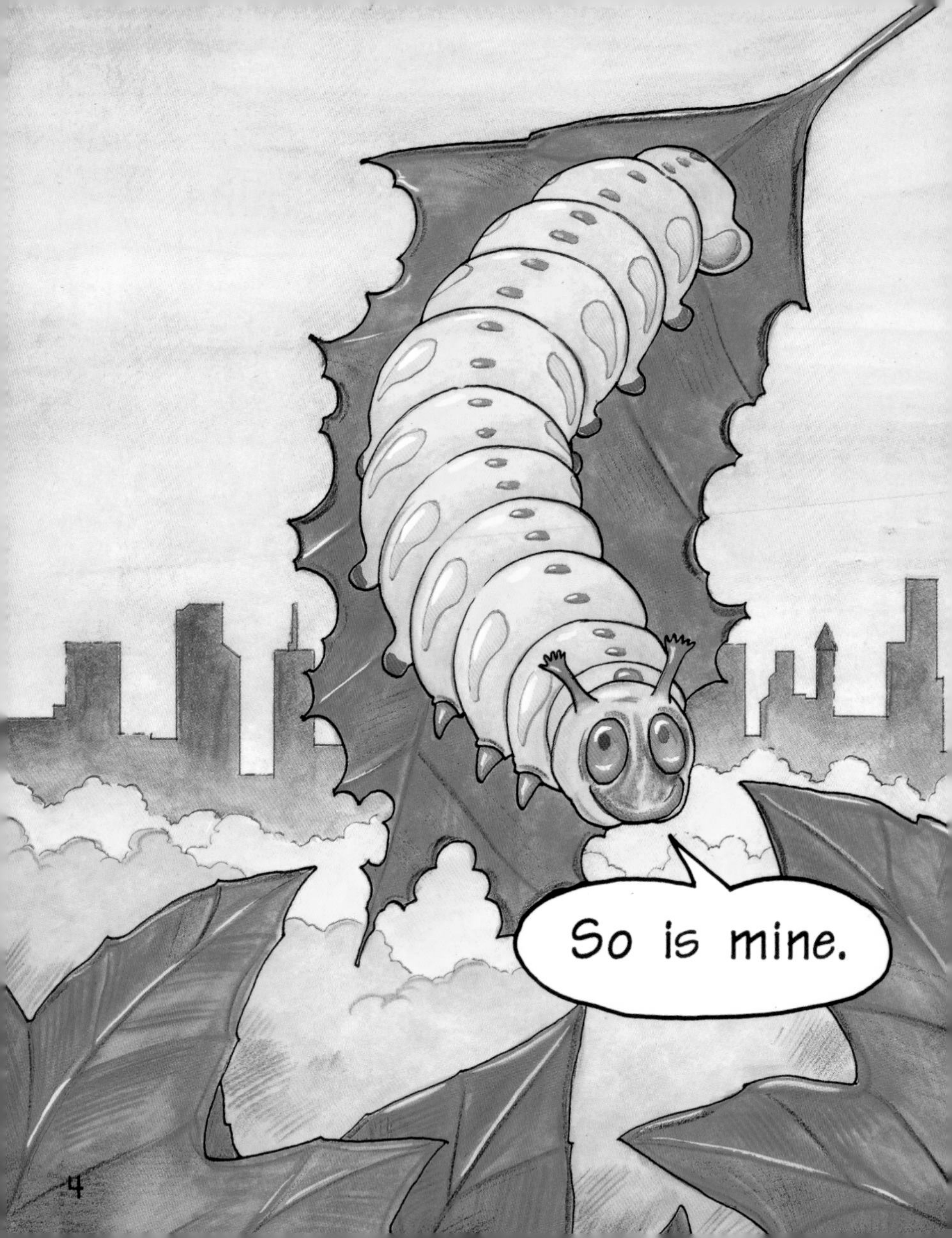
So is mine.

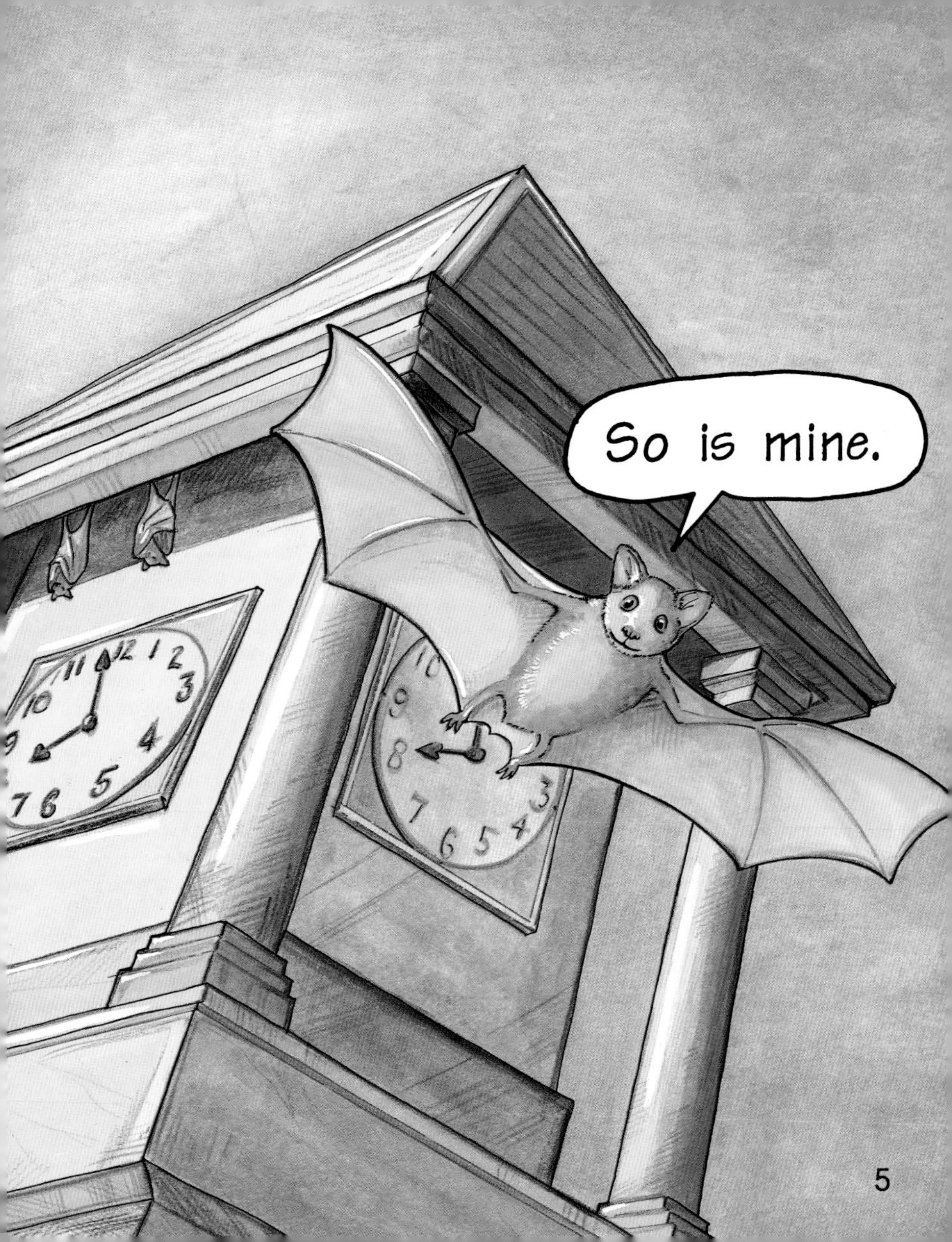
So is mine.

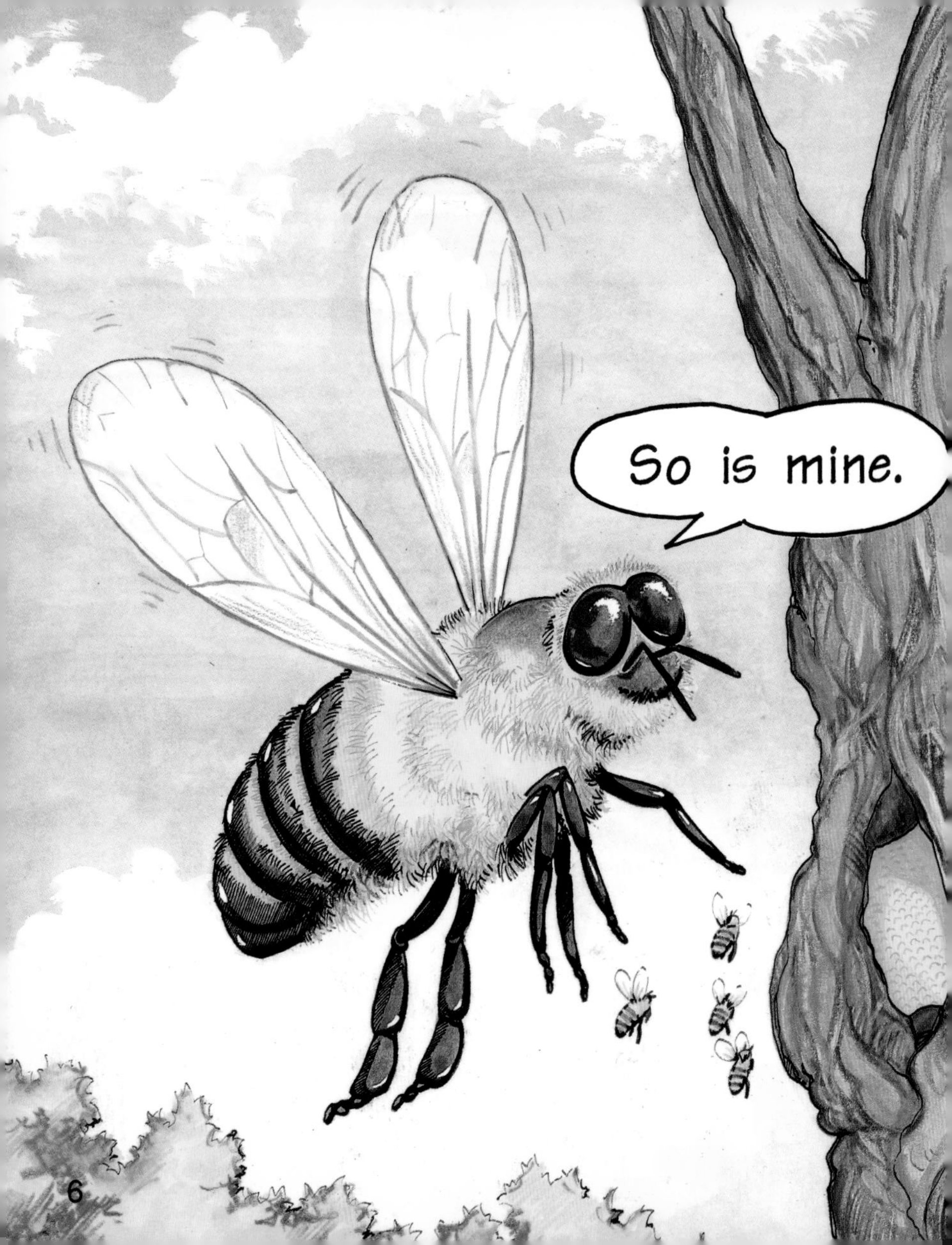
So is mine.

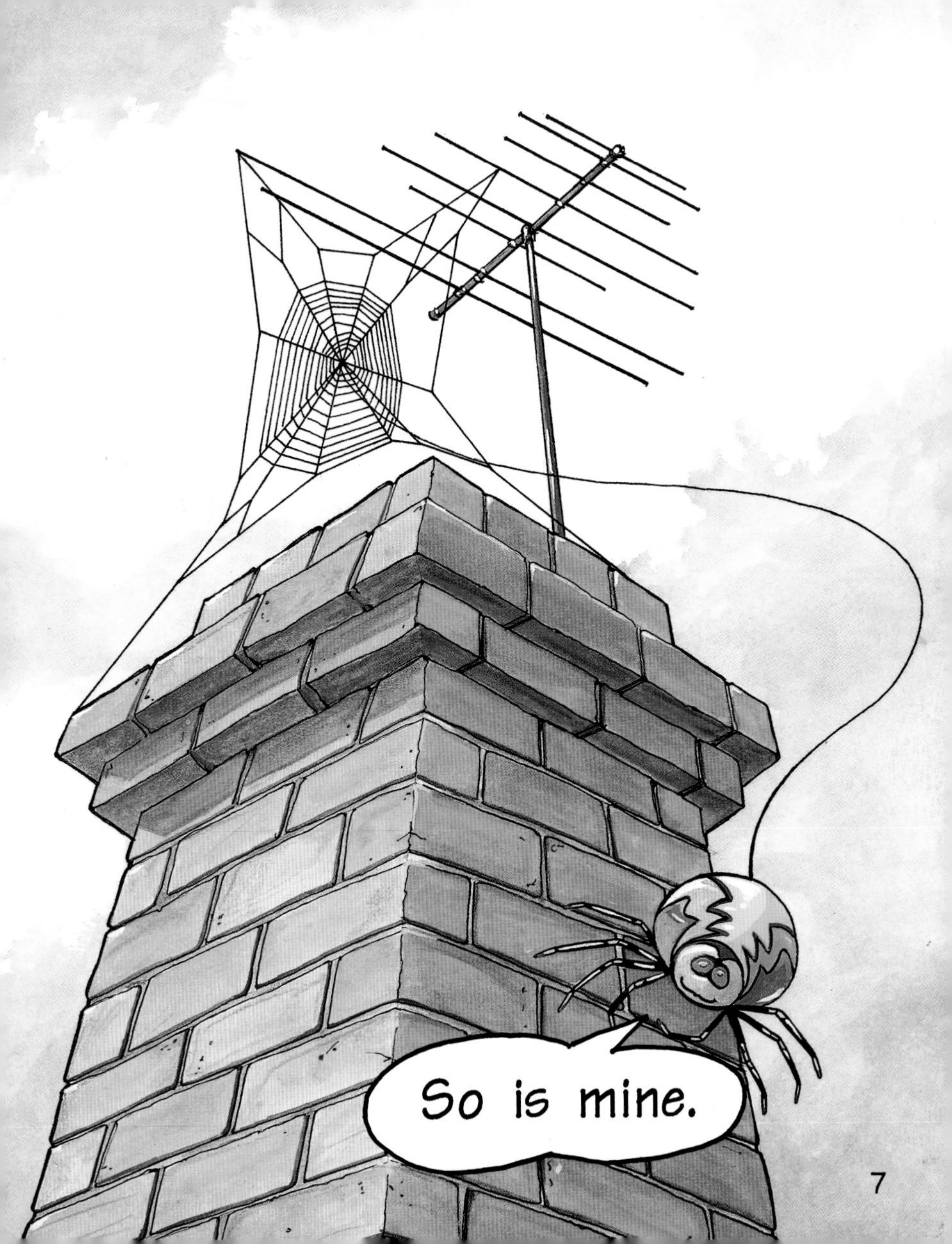
So is mine.

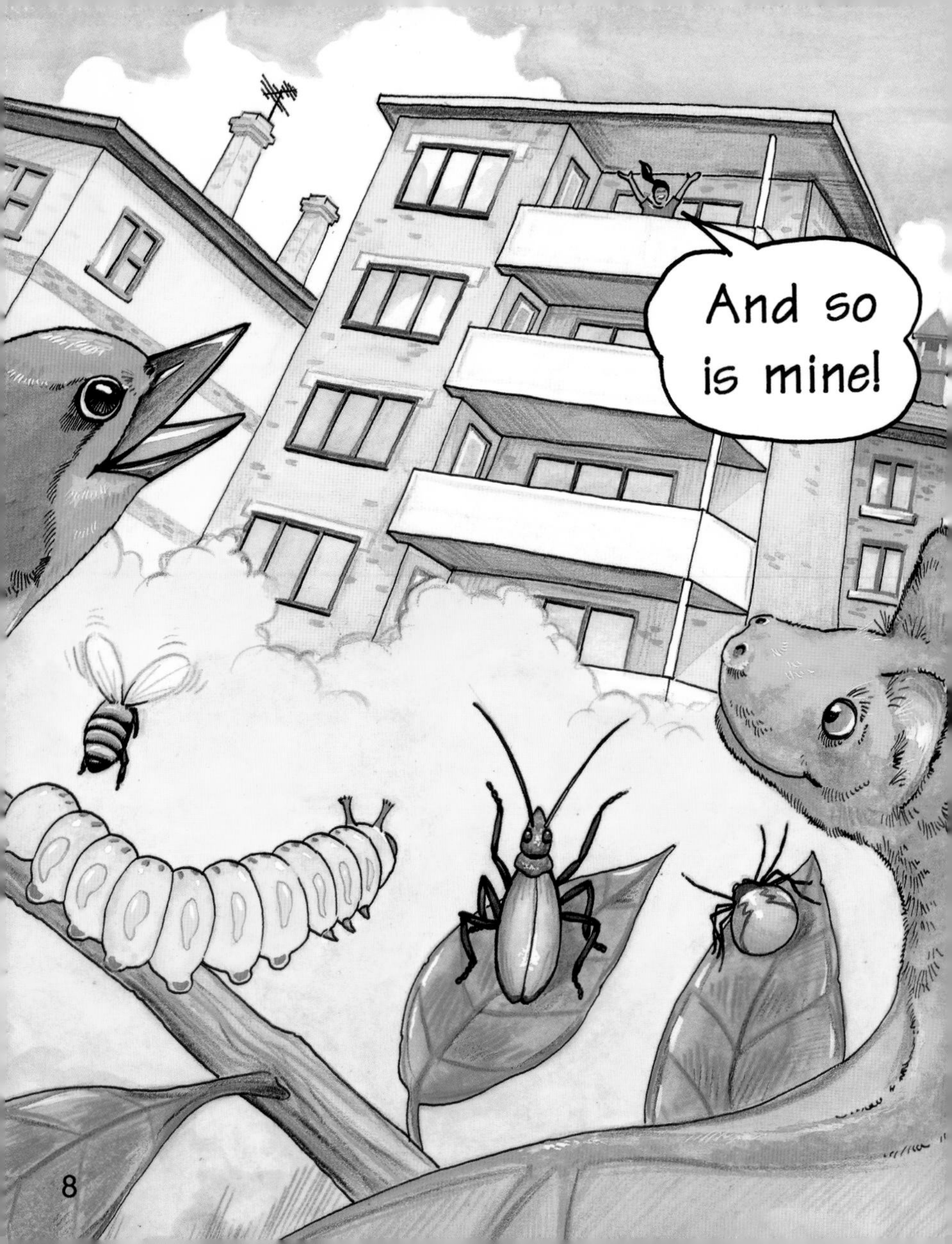
And so is mine!